TO ....

FROM ....

D0966485

DECEMBER 31

PEANUTS®

Enjoy the blessing!

Revel in the goodness!

PSALM 128:2 The Message

DECEMBER 30

DECEMBER 29

JANUARY 2

DECEMBER 28

JANUARY 3

DECEMBER 27

FRiends
make time
for the
truly important
things in life.

JANUARY 4

DECEMBER 26

JANUARY 5

On earth

PEACE,

good will toward men.

LUKE 2:14 KJV

DECEMBER 25

JANUARY 6

DECEMBER 24

I...THINK OF YOU and GIVE THANKS.

EPHESIANS 1:16
The Message

DECEMBER 23

DECEMBER 22

JANUARY 9

DECEMBER 21

JANUARY 10

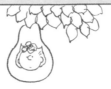

PEANUTS by Schulz

"FOUR CALLING BIRDS, AND A PARTRIDGE IN A PEAR TREE..."

THAT SONG DRIVES ME CRAZY!

WHAT IN THE WORLD IS A "CALLING BIRD"?

A CALLING BIRD IS A KIND OF PARTRIDGE..

IN I SAMUEL, 26:20, IT SAYS, "FOR THE KING OF ISRAEL HAS COME OUT TO SEEK MY LIFE JUST AS THOUGH HE WERE HUNTING THE CALLING BIRD..."

THERE'S A PLAY ON WORDS HERE, YOU SEE.. DAVID WAS STANDING ON A MOUNTAIN CALLING, AND HE COMPARED HIMSELF TO A PARTRIDGE BEING HUNTED...

ISN'T THAT FASCINATING?

IF I GET SOCKS AGAIN FOR CHRISTMAS THIS YEAR, I'LL GO EVEN MORE CRAZY!

12-21-97

DECEMBER 20

JANUARY 11

DECEMBER 19

JANUARY 12

JANUARY 13

DECEMBER 17

Just wanted to **BRIGHTEN** your day—

You've brightened **so many** of mine!

JANUARY 14

DECEMBER 16

The one who BLESSES OTHERS is ABUNDANTLY blessed. PROVERBS 11:25
The Message

JANUARY 15

DECEMBER 15

JANUARY 16

DECEMBER 14

JANUARY 17

DECEMBER 13

JANUARY 18

DECEMBER 12

JANUARY 19

DECEMBER 11

JANUARY 20

DECEMBER 10

Our
mouths
were filled
with
LAUGHTER.

PSALM 126:2 NIV

JANUARY 21

JANUARY 22

DECEMBER 8

JANUARY 23

DECEMBER 7

JANUARY 24

DECEMBER 6

JANUARY 25

DECEMBER 5

JANUARY 26

DECEMBER 4

JANUARY 27

DECEMBER 3

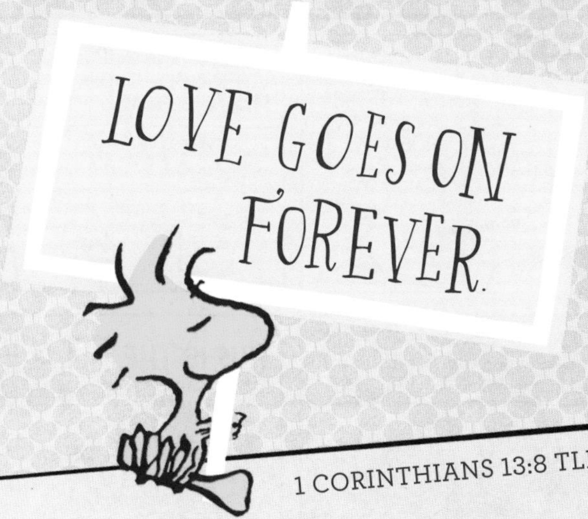

1 CORINTHIANS 13:8 TLB

JANUARY 28

DECEMBER 2

PEANUTS

DO YOU GET AN ALLOWANCE, CHARLIE BROWN?

NOT REALLY... BUT I GET FIFTEEN CENTS A WEEK FOR FEEDING THE DOG..

WELL! THAT MAKES **ME** FEEL KIND OF IMPORTANT...

BY CREATING WORK, I AM HELPING TO BOLSTER OUR ECONOMY!

4-25

SCHULZ

JANUARY 29

One thing's
for sure—
you're in
good
hands
and
caring
thoughts!

DECEMBER 1

JANUARY 30

NOVEMBER 30

JANUARY 31

NOVEMBER 29

FEBRUARY 1

NOVEMBER 28

FEBRUARY 2

In
EVERYTHING
give thanks.

I THESSALONIANS 5:18 KJV

NOVEMBER 27

Follow
the Way
of Love.

I CORINTHIANS 14:1 NIV

FEBRUARY 3

NOVEMBER 26

FEBRUARY 4

NOVEMBER 25

FEBRUARY 5

Giving Thanks for you.

EPHESIANS 1:16 NIV

NOVEMBER 24

FEBRUARY 6

PEANUTS by Schulz

SO ISAAC WAS SAVED

THEN, GUESS WHAT HAPPENED..

ABRAHAM TURNED AROUND, AND SAW THIS POOR RAM..

IT HAD ITS HORNS CAUGHT IN A THICKET.. DID HE SET IT FREE? OF COURSE NOT!

© 1982 United Feature Syndicate, Inc.

HE OFFERED IT UP AS A BURNT OFFERING! CAN YOU IMAGINE THAT?! HE KILLED IT!!

HEY, SNOOPY, WE'RE INVITED OVER TO GRAMMA'S HOUSE FOR THANKSGIVING DINNER..

11-22

AND YOU KNOW WHAT THEY'RE GOING TO EAT? A BIRD!!

BLEAH!

HE'S NOT COMING ALONG?

DON'T ASK ME WHY.. I NEVER KNOW WHAT HE'S THINKING..

NOVEMBER 23

Friends are double the fun... & double the blessings!

FEBRUARY 7

PEANUTS

HERE YOU ARE, SNOOPY...HAPPY THANKSGIVING!

Tm. Reg. U. S. Pat. Off.—All rights reserved
© 1967 by United Feature Syndicate, Inc.

11-23

THANK YOU

NO CRANBERRIES?

SCHULZ.

NOVEMBER 22

A FRIEND LOVES AT ALL TIMES.

PROVERBS 17:17 NIV

FEBRUARY 8

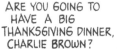

11-28 © 1985 United Feature Syndicate, Inc.

NOVEMBER 21

FEBRUARY 9

NOVEMBER 20

FEBRUARY 10

NOVEMBER 19

FEBRUARY 11

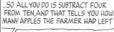

NOVEMBER 18

"Your eyes are beautiful," he said.

"Shall I compare them to a summer day? No, even more."

8-29

"Your eyes are like two supper dishes."

FEBRUARY 12

No wonder

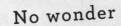
MY HEART

is filled with joy.

ACTS 2:26 TLB

NOVEMBER 17

FEBRUARY 13

I BOUGHT THIS VALENTINE CANDY FOR THE LITTLE RED HAIRED GIRL, BUT I WAS TOO SHY TO GIVE IT TO HER ...

I'D GIVE IT TO YOU, BUT CHOCOLATE ISN'T GOOD FOR DOGS..

I COULD JUST PICK OUT THE CARAMELS..

© 1989 United Feature Syndicate, Inc.

FEBRUARY 14

NOVEMBER 15

FEBRUARY 15

NOVEMBER 14

LOVE is patient,
LOVE is kind.

1 CORINTHIANS 13:4 NIV

FEBRUARY 16

NOVEMBER 13

FEBRUARY 17

the storms of life
are no match for good friends.

NOVEMBER 12

FEBRUARY 18

NOVEMBER 11

FEBRUARY 19

NOVEMBER 10

Wouldn't it be nice if life were like a DVD...
And you could *fast-forward* through crummy times.

FEBRUARY 20

NOVEMBER 9

Peace be with you.

JOHN 20:21 NIV

FEBRUARY 21

NOVEMBER 8

FEBRUARY 22

FEBRUARY 23

NOVEMBER 6

FEBRUARY 24

NOVEMBER 5

FEBRUARY 25

NOVEMBER 4

FEBRUARY 26

NOVEMBER 3

You can't go wrong
when you **love** others.

ROMANS 13:10
The Message

FEBRUARY 27

FEBRUARY 28

NOVEMBER 1

FEBRUARY 29

OCTOBER 31

MARCH 1

Let's
CELEBRATE
and be
festive.

PSALM 118:24
The Message

OCTOBER 30

MARCH 2

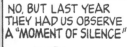

MARCH 3

OCTOBER 28

MARCH 4

OCTOBER 27

MARCH 5

OCTOBER 26

I PRAY

that you might enjoy

good health.

III JOHN 1:2 NIV

MARCH 6

OCTOBER 25

MARCH 7

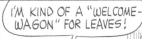

OCTOBER 24

We've definitely got what it takes to enjoy life.

MARCH 8

YOU'RE NEAT

YOU'RE SWEET

YOU'RE A TREAT!

OCTOBER 23

FOR "SHOW AND TELL" TODAY, I HAVE BROUGHT MY NEW "PRAYING DOLL"

3-21

YOU WILL NOTE THAT HER HANDS ARE HELD TOGETHER IN A PRAYING POSITION BY VELCRO.. ARE THERE ANY QUESTIONS?

NO, I DO NOT BELIEVE VELCRO IS MENTIONED ANYWHERE IN THE NEW TESTAMENT

SCHULZ

MARCH 9

OCTOBER 22

MARCH 10

PEANUTS
by SCHULZ

YES, MA'AM...I'M READY...

THIS IS MY REPORT ON AUTUMN..

WHEN AUTUMN COMES, THE LEAVES BEGIN TO FALL...

NOW, I NEED A VOLUNTEER FROM THE CLASS...HOW ABOUT YOU? THE STUPID LOOKING KID IN THE FRONT ROW..

ALL RIGHT, LET'S SAY THIS KID IS WALKING THROUGH THE WOODS..

SUDDENLY, THE LEAVES BEGIN TO FALL..

IT'S AUTUMN !!

THANKS, KID! YOU WERE GREAT! JUST STAY AWAY FROM ANYONE WHO HAS A RAKE..

10-10

© 1993 United Feature Syndicate, Inc.

MARCH 11

You have

FILLED

my heart with
greater joy.

PSALM 4:7 NIV

OCTOBER 20

MARCH 12

OCTOBER 19

PEANUTS

I'LL BE ON YOUR TEAM, CHARLIE BROWN, IF YOU WON'T MAKE ME WEAR A CAP..

I DON'T LIKE TO WEAR A CAP BECAUSE IT COVERS UP MY HAIR...I HAVE NATURALLY CURLY HAIR, YOU KNOW

I DON'T SUPPOSE YOU'VE EVER HAD A PLAYER ON YOUR TEAM WHO HAS HAD NATURALLY CURLY HAIR, HAVE YOU, CHARLIE BROWN?

3-30

NO, BUT I'VE HAD MY SHARE OF OTHER PECULIAR KINDS!

Schulz

MARCH 13

OCTOBER 18

YOUR LOVE HAS GIVEN ME GREAT JOY.

PHILEMON 1:7 NIV

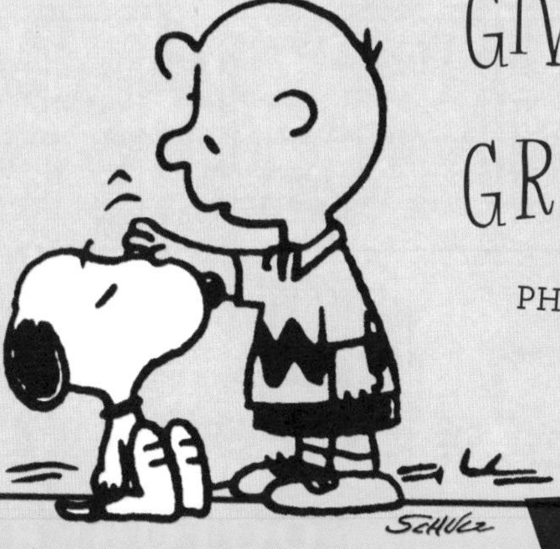

MARCH 14

OCTOBER 17

MARCH 15

OCTOBER 16

MARCH 16

OCTOBER 15

MARCH 17

OCTOBER 14

MARCH 18

OCTOBER 13

MARCH 19

OCTOBER 12

MARCH 20

OCTOBER 11

MARCH 21

CELEBRATE
with
GReAt joy.

NEHEMIAH 8:12 NIV

OCTOBER 10

MARCH 22

OCTOBER 9

BE HAPPY...

and let your heart

give you joy.

ECCLESIATES 11:9 NIV

MARCH 23

OCTOBER 8

MARCH 24

OCTOBER 7

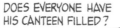

MARCH 25

There are lots of reasons today is *Special* and they all begin with YOU!

OCTOBER 6

MARCH 26

OCTOBER 5

OCTOBER 4

MARCH 28

OCTOBER 3

MARCH 29

OCTOBER 2

HaPPY...

MARCH 30

My cup
OVERflows
with blessings.

PSALM 23:5 NLT

OCTOBER 1

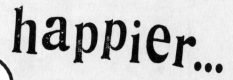

happier...

MARCH 31

SEPTEMBER 30

happiest!

APRIL 1

SEPTEMBER 29

APRIL 2

SEPTEMBER 28

SEPTEMBER 27

APRIL 4

A
Sweet friendship
refreshes the soul.

PROVERBS 27:9
The Message

SEPTEMBER 26

APRIL 5

SEPTEMBER 25

Rejoice
and be
glad.

PSALM 118:24 TLB

APRIL 6

SEPTEMBER 24

APRIL 7

SEPTEMBER 23

APRIL 8

SEPTEMBER 22

APRIL 9

SEPTEMBER 21

Your love
has given me

GREAT JOY

ENCOURAGEMENT.

PHILEMON 1:7 NIV

APRIL 10

Do You ever wish Life came with A great Big 'do-over' Button?

SEPTEMBER 20

APRIL 11

SEPTEMBER 19

APRIL 12

SEPTEMBER 18

APRIL 13

PEANUTS
by Schulz

"TEAL"?

"TEAL" OR "CERULEAN"...WHICH COLOR EXPRESSES WHAT I'M TRYING TO SAY HERE?

DOES "WILD STRAWBERRY" SAY ANYTHING AT ALL?

AND I'M NOT SURE IF "FUCHSIA" MAKES AN EFFORT TO COMMUNICATE..

9-2

WHICH REALLY SPEAKS LOUDER, "TANGERINE" OR "DANDELION"?

IN FACT, DOES "ROYAL PURPLE" SAY WHAT WE...

COLOR THE SKY BLUE AND THE GRASS GREEN!

GET OUT THE "BLACK", I'LL DO A NIGHT SCENE..

© 1990 United Feature Syndicate, Inc.

SEPTEMBER 17

APRIL 14

SEPTEMBER 16

FRiENDS

make the good stuff

even better.

APRIL 15

SEPTEMBER 15

SEPTEMBER 14

APRIL 17

SEPTEMBER 13

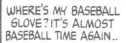

APRIL 18

Most of all,

LET LOVE

guide your life.

COLOSSIANS 3:14 TLB

SEPTEMBER 12

APRIL 19

SEPTEMBER 11

APRIL 20

SEPTEMBER 10

APRIL 21

PEANUTS
by Schulz

YES, MA'AM.. I'M MORE THAN READY

THIS IS MY REPORT ON THE FOOTBALL CAREER OF MOSES..

YES, MA'AM.. THAT MOSES.. YOU DIDN'T?

ANYWAY, WHEN MOSES WAS YOUNG, HE SHOWED GREAT PROMISE..ALL THE PROFESSIONAL TEAMS WANTED HIM..

YES, MA'AM.. FOOTBALL TEAMS..

WELL, WE ALL KNOW HOW HE WENT UP ON THE MOUNTAIN, AND THEN CARRIED THOSE TABLETS OF STONE BACK DOWN..

THIS PROBABLY WAS HOW HE HURT HIS THROWING ARM..AFTER THAT, HE COULD NEVER THROW THE LONG BALL..

HE COULD ONLY THROW A FEW SHORT SIDELINE PATTERNS..

PRETTY SOON HE GOT INVOLVED IN OTHER THINGS AND QUIT FOOTBALL..

RESEARCH? NO, MA'AM...MY GRAMPA...WELL, I FIGURE HE MUST HAVE KNOWN HIM..

I GUESS GRAMPA ISN'T AS OLD AS I THOUGHT HE WAS..

10-18

SEPTEMBER 9

APRIL 22

SEPTEMBER 8

APRIL 23

WHAT WOULD YOU SAY IF I TOLD YOU I WAS GOING TO DEVOTE THE REST OF MY LIFE TO MAKING YOU HAPPY?

WE'LL GO FOR LONG WALKS IN THE WOODS AND ROMP AROUND IN THE YARD...

YOU'LL SIT IN MY LAP, AND I'LL SCRATCH YOUR EARS, AND WE'LL WATCH TV AND I'LL GIVE YOU COOKIES...

WHAT KIND OF COOKIES?

10-26

SEPTEMBER 7

Sometimes it takes just a little *seed of faith*... to make the BLESSINGS BLOOM!

APRIL 24

SEPTEMBER 6

If we hope
  for what we
  do not yet have,

we wait for it
  patiently.

ROMANS 8:25 NIV

APRIL 25

SEPTEMBER 5

APRIL 26

SEPTEMBER 4

APRIL 27

SEPTEMBER 3

APRIL 28

POWER

to those who are

tired and worn out.

ISAIAH 40:29 NLT

SEPTEMBER 2

APRIL 29

SEPTEMBER 1

APRIL 30

AUGUST 31

MAY 1

You have a very

SPECIAL

place in my heart.

PHILIPPIANS 1:7 TLB

AUGUST 30

MAY 2

AUGUST 29

MAY 3

AUGUST 28

MAY 4

AUGUST 27

We never get
tired of watching
DANCING WITH THE BEAGLES.

MAY 5

AUGUST 26

The
sweetness
of a...
friend
gives delight.

PROVERBS 27:9 NKJV

MAY 6

AUGUST 25

MAY 7

So
HAPPY
for
YOU!

So
CLAPPY
for
YOU!

AUGUST 24

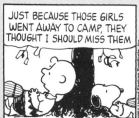

MAY 8

I CAN'T HELP YOU WITH YOUR HOMEWORK TONIGHT.. I WANT TO WATCH THIS PROGRAM...

THEN I SHALL SEEK ELSEWHERE FOR A SPIRITUAL CLOAK TO SHIELD ME FROM MY TEACHER'S ICY WRATH..

10-31

HERE.. WE'RE SUPPOSED TO DO ALL OF THESE PROBLEMS ON PAGE NINE..

© 1995 United Feature Syndicate, Inc.

AUGUST 23

MAY 9

AUGUST 22

MAY 10

AUGUST 21

Live a life
of
LOVE.

EPHESIANS 5:2 NIV

MAY 11

AUGUST 20

MAY 12

AUGUST 19

MAY 13

A true friend
STICKS
by you.

PROVERBS 18:24
The Message

AUGUST 18

MAY 14

AUGUST 17

MAY 15

AUGUST 16

MAY 16

AUGUST 15

PEANUTS

THEY CAN'T FIRE MISS OTHMAR!

I'LL WRITE A LETTER OF PROTEST! I'LL BLOW THIS THING WIDE OPEN!!

I'LL WRITE TO SOMEONE IN AUTHORITY! SOMEONE WHO CAN REALLY DO SOMETHING!

HOW DOES ONE GO ABOUT GETTING A LETTER TO THE APOSTLE PAUL?

MAY 17

AUGUST 14

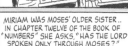

MAY 18

AUGUST 13

FAITH

is holding on

tight

when the going

gets windy.

MAY 19

LOVE builds up.

I CORINTHIANS 8:1 NIV

AUGUST 12

MAY 20

AUGUST 11

MAY 21

AUGUST 10

MAY 22

AUGUST 9

MAY 23

AUGUST 8

MAY 24

AUGUST 7

MAY 25

AUGUST 6

NOTHING

will be impossible

for you.

MATTHEW 17:20 NIV

MAY 26

AUGUST 5

MAY 27

AUGUST 4

MAY 28

AUGUST 3

MAY 29

AUGUST 2

MAY 30

Rejoice ALWAYS !

I THESSALONIANS 5:16 KJV

AUGUST 1

"I used to think you were a great engineer," she said.

"Once, I even loved you..."

"But you've gotten too big for your bridges."

MAY 31

PEANUTS by Schulz

TODAY'S THE BIG DAY!

I LOVE GRADUATION, DON'T YOU, SIR?

WHAT DO WE HAVE TO DO?

JUST MARCH DOWN THE AISLE, AND WALK UP TO THE PRINCIPAL...

WHEN HE HANDS YOU YOUR DIPLOMA, SAY, "THANK YOU"

LISTEN TO THAT MUSIC, MARCIE...

THEY'RE CALLING OUR NAMES, SIR...

SOMEONE SHOULD HAVE A TALK WITH OUR PRINCIPAL...

OTHER SCHOOLS PLAY "POMP AND CIRCUMSTANCE" FOR GRADUATION...

I HATE GOING DOWN THE AISLE DOING THE "HOKEY POKEY"!

JUNE 1

JULY 30

I'M TIRED OF BEING WISHY-WASHY! I'M GONNA WALK RIGHT OVER, AND TALK TO THAT LITTLE RED-HAIRED GIRL!

I'M DOING IT! I'M COMMITTED! NOTHING CAN STOP ME NOW!

© 1986 United Feature Syndicate, Inc.

ABSOLUTELY NOTHING!

1-15

JUNE 2

JULY 29

JUNE 3

JULY 28

You have shown

GREAT

kindness.

1 KINGS 3:6 NIV

JUNE 4

JULY 27

DIGGING FOR RARE EGYPTIAN COINS CAN BE VERY EXCITING...

IF YOU FIND THE RIGHT ONES, YOU COULD MAKE A FORTUNE..

1-9-86 © 1985 United Feature Syndicate, Inc.

ALL IT TAKES IS FAITH AND PATIENCE

UNLESS, OF COURSE, IT SUDDENLY OCCURS TO YOU THAT YOU'RE IN THE WRONG DESERT..

JUNE 5

I...have gained

MUCH JOY

and comfort

from your love.

PHILEMON 1:7 TLB

JULY 26

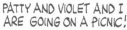

JUNE 6

JULY 25

JULY 24

JUNE 8

PEANUTS
by Schulz

"AND NOW IT'S TIME FOR OUR BIBLE QUIZ"

"AND THE FIRST TO CALL IN THE CORRECT ANSWER WILL RECEIVE FOUR TICKETS TO THE UPCOMING JONI JAMES CONCERT!"

"HERE IS THE QUESTION... 'WHAT DID SAMUEL CALL THE NAME OF THE STONE THAT HE SET BETWEEN MIZPEH AND SHEN?'"

"EBENEZER!" FIRST BOOK OF SAMUEL, CHAPTER SEVEN, TWELFTH VERSE!

OH, SURE...HE'S THE CUTE ONE... SURE, I KNOW..

SURE, HE'S CUTE, TOO.. I MEAN, YOU KNOW, LIKE, SURE...

WELL, I MEAN, WHO ELSE? COME ON! I MEAN, SURE...

"THAT'S CORRECT, MA'AM! CONGRATULATIONS"

A CONTEST, HUH? YOU SHOULD HAVE CALLED IN..

JULY 23

JUNE 9

JULY 22

JUNE 10

We LOVE ONE ANOTHER.

II JOHN 1:5 KJV

JULY 21

GOOD MORNING, GANG... WELCOME TO BIBLE CLASS..

MY NAME IS SALLY, AND BECAUSE I'M BIGGER THAN YOU, I'M GOING TO BE YOUR TEACHER...

I WAS HOPING WE'D GET A CUTE CHICK...SO WHAT DO WE GET? AN OLD LADY!

5-28

SCHULZ

JULY 20

JUNE 12

JULY 19

She laughs
with no fear
of the
FUTURE.

PROVERBS 31:25 NLT

Schulz

JUNE 13

JULY 18

JUNE 14

TODAY WE'RE GOING TO TALK A LITTLE ABOUT THE SEA OF GALILEE...

GATSBY STOOD BY THE SEA OF GALILEE, AND PICKED OUT THE GREEN LIGHT AT THE END OF DAISY'S DOCK..

5-31

© 1991 United Feature Syndicate, Inc.

DO YOU LIVE AROUND HERE, KID?

JUNE 15

JULY 16

JUNE 16

Oh,
thank you...

you are

SO GOOD

to me.

RUTH 2:13 TLB

JULY 15

JUNE 17

JULY 14

JUNE 18

JULY 13

JUNE 19

JULY 12

Love is kind.

I CORINTHIANS 13:4 NIV

Schulz

JUNE 20

JULY 11

JUNE 21

JULY 10

JUNE 22

JULY 9

JUNE 23

8-15

JULY 8

HATS OFF TO YOU!

JULY 7

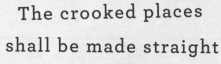

The crooked places
shall be made straight
&
the rough places smooth.

ISAIAH 40:4 NKJV

JUNE 25

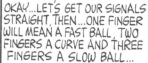

JUNE 26

JULY 5

JUNE 27

JULY 4

JUNE 28

JULY 3

JUNE 29

JULY 2

JUNE 30